ALICE & TWINKLE

Alice meets Twinkle

Four stories about
Alice and her Angel Twinkle

Amanda Tooke

First published in Great Britain by Amanda Tooke

www.theangelmystic.co.uk

ISBN: 978-1-913898-40-3

Page layout and book production
Pixel Tweaks
www.pixeltweakspublications.com

Illustrations by Alison Brown
www.alibrowncreative.co.uk

To Fliss and Delilah, my beautiful granddaughters who have taught me so much and give me such joy.

May this book help you and many other children too.

I wrote this book from my experience of working at Social Services and hearing what can go on behind close doors.

So many children need to know they are not alone and have Angels to help them in every day situations.

It also shares some simple examples of the power of positivity and Law of Attraction.

Amanda Tooke

STORY ONE
Mean Friends

"Come on Alice, time for bed," said mum.

Alice was not happy; it had not been a good day at school. One of the boys in her class had been really mean to her and Alice was so sad that all the usual things she loved to do didn't cheer her up.

As she was getting ready for bed in her bedroom, mum helped Alice to tidy up the mess – Alice always seemed to be able to make a mess whatever she did.

Toys, clothes and books were everywhere.

Alice has soft, red, wavy hair. It was often wild - always wanting to do its own thing (a bit like Alice). Alice loved how it felt when the wind blew through it as she ran around outside.

As mum brushed Alice's hair, she could see that Alice was sad - she asked, "What's wrong? you don't seem very happy today darling?"

"Nothing" replied Alice, she really didn't want to talk about it and remember how sad she felt.

Alice went to wash her face, looking in the mirror she could see freckles that speckled over her nose. She started remembering how she used to rub and rub hoping they would go away.

One day her nana told her that they were one of the things that added to her beauty and made her special. "No-one is ever meant to be the same Alice" her nana said. "Learn to fall in love with all of you. You are perfect and gorgeous just as you are, exactly as you are meant to be." Alice could never look at her freckles again without remembering that.

Time spent with nana was full of fun and there always seemed to be an adventure to be had when she was with her. The stories she told were the best.

As her mum tucked Alice up in bed, she placed her favourite bear Ari next to her.

Ari had been given to Alice when she was a baby by her dad's friend who was visiting them and had been everywhere with her ever since. He was getting a bit tatty looking now, with a squashed nose as Alice often fell asleep on him but it didn't matter as he always made her feel better.

Tonight, more than ever she needed that comfort and smell of Ari to get away the thoughts of the bad day and the mean classmate.

As Mum said goodnight, turned the light down low and quietly left the room, Alice sighed and hugged Ari even tighter.

She lay in her bed but all she could think about was that mean boy who said she couldn't join in hide and seek because she had red hair. Tears started to wash down her face and onto Ari.

Why was he so mean? What is wrong with her wild red hair? She felt so different and left out.

Sobbing into Ari she was so, so sad.

As Alice opened her eyes, she thought she was seeing things! There were sparkly lights at the end of her bed. She looked around her room wondering where they were coming from.

Alice stopped crying; she was fascinated looking at the lights. They made her feel calm and so comforted. But what were they?

As she watched the white sparkly lights flicker, she felt like she knew what they were even though nobody had told her.

They soothed her and made her smile. Alice felt like she wanted to thank the lights for being there and making her feel better. She remembered again about being different and that being different was ok, it is the way everyone is supposed to be. Not sure where the thoughts came from, but they made her feel better.

The lights were relaxing her as she lay in her warm cosy bed. Memories of the bad day and mean boy left, Alice started to look at it differently.

Maybe he was not that mean, Alice thought. Maybe he was in a bad mood himself or worried or scared of something.

Mum had told her before that sometimes people behave badly because they are feeling bad themselves and are then mean to others. That gave her even more comfort and she was soon fast asleep dreaming of what these lights might be.

That night Alice learnt that there really is more to this world than what we realise.

STORY TWO

I can't do it

"Alice wakey, wakey, sleepy head, time for school," her mum called for the third time that morning.

Alice was having such a lovely dream in bed, and she didn't want to wake up. She often had funny dreams but had come to understand that no matter how crazy they were it was always about how they made her feel. Her nana had told her that messages can be hidden in dreams. Just like the one when she was flying over the roof tops and she felt so free and adventurous.

After a big stretch Alice pulled the duvet straight. She gave Ari a quick squeeze before sitting him up on her pillow that had little cutest fairies on it.

She went into the bright white bathroom to get ready for school. Looking at the stripey towels hanging on the towel rail she remembered it was Tuesday and that meant PE! Her heart sank and tummy flipped, she did NOT like PE day.

Whilst Alice loved running around and being outside, she couldn't catch a ball no matter how hard she tried and the whole class knew it. No one ever picked her to be on their team. Team games were just not her thing.

Alice was a free spirit who liked to do her own thing and not follow rules. This made school hard at times for her. She started to think about all the times she had been last in the row to be picked for a team, it was seen as the unlucky team if Alice was on it, it was so embarrassing. Tuesday was the worst day of the week, she had decided.

Standing on her step at the bathroom sink, Alice could look into the mirror and see the reflection of her standing there in her pink unicorn pyjamas.

Her hair was all messy and wild from sleeping. She splashed her face with water to wake herself up and brushed her teeth.

Alice had a gap where the front two had come out and now her big new teeth had started to pop through.

She sniffed at the strawberry handwash as her mum came into the bathroom standing behind her all dressed and ready for work.

"Good morning sleepy head" said mum planting a big kiss on the top of her wild flame hair.

"How are you today darling?"

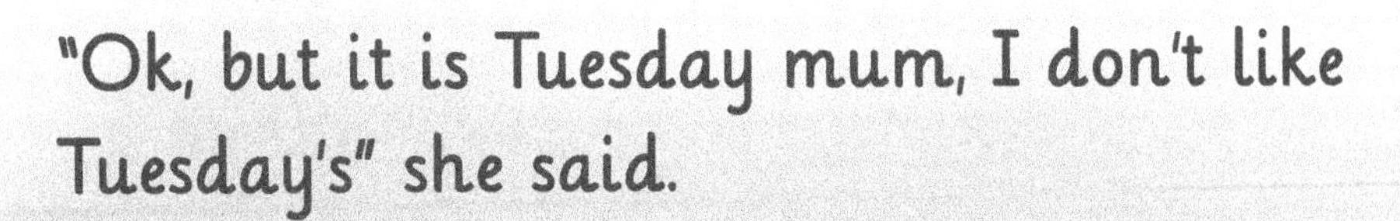

"Ok, but it is Tuesday mum, I don't like Tuesday's" she said.

"That's not true" her mum said. "For it to be true you would have to not like any Tuesday, but you loved Tuesday when it was your birthday last year and we went to the Zoo with your friends. You also loved the Tuesdays in the school holidays when you played with your friends all day long and when we went to Anglesey to stay in the caravan with your brother and dad, didn't you?"

"Well, yes" Alice said. "But it's PE today and nobody ever picks me, I hate it. I'm stupid".

"Oh Alice" says mum, "you are not a team sports person, but you are not stupid, you swim like a fish! You are an amazing dancer and gymnast but just because you are not good at catching a ball doesn't change how fantastic you are.

Some people who are great at catching balls and playing rounders can't do what you can do, we are all good at different things. That's what makes life and people interesting. Life is not a competition Alice, even if some people think it is."

"PE is one hour out of your day that you don't like playing rounders in, not the whole of Tuesday. You have art today, don't you? You love that!

You have swimming later as well, so Tuesday is not all bad. I have your favourite pasta in for tea so you can look forward to that later too."

Alice started to feel a bit better, her mum picked up her purple hairbrush and asked her how she wanted her hair today. "Ponytail, please mum" she said smiling and she started to feel more excited about the day.

"Ok are you ready to say your affirmations?" her mum said brushing her hair into a ponytail.

"I am," said Alice

"I am smart, I am clever, I am kind.

I am powerful and can achieve whatever I want when I set my mind."

"Yes, you can" her mum said. – Alice had been saying affirmations with her mum for as long as she could remember.

"You can catch the ball to if you decide to. Everything you want to achieve starts in here." She whispered softly tapping the top of her head.

Alice thought to herself Tuesday wasn't going to be that bad at all. On the way to school, she kept saying in her head 'I can catch the ball; I can catch the ball'

I am smart,
I am clever,
I am kind.
I am powerful
and can
achieve
whatever I
want when I
set my mind.

When it came to PE, she did exactly that - much to everyone's amazement. She caught the ball and even scored a rounder. Everyone cheered and shouted well done, Alice!

At the end of the game the other team captain said "Next week I will pick you for my team Alice"

Alice couldn't help but smile as on this day she learnt that it is really important to choose the right words so instead of saying 'I can't 'in future she will say 'I can' and 'I will'.

Alice likes Tuesdays!

STORY THREE

Thunder and lightning

Alice's dad worked away quite a lot, so it was often just Alice, her mum and her little pesky brother in the week. Now whilst he was often annoying and cried and wanted to do whatever she was doing she loved him a lot. She loved helping her mum take care of him and could always make him giggle.

Billy looked so different to Alice with his blond straight hair and chubby legs, he always seemed to have a graze on his knee from falling over (Mostly from mischief when he was trying to do things he shouldn't be doing).

Alice felt very protective of her little brother Billy and always kept an eye out for him.

It was a usual Wednesday evening but something was just not right, Alice could feel it.

She always knew somehow when something was going to happen, she could feel it in her tummy. She never told anyone about the feelings as they were hard to describe.

This particular Wednesday they were having sausage and mash for tea. It was Billy's favourite with yummy gravy. If they were really lucky mum would add a Yorkshire pudding on their plates too.

That feeling in her tummy was not going away even with lovely sausage and mash to fill it.

It had been a lovely warm sunny day, but it felt heavy and no air as mum called it.

"There could be a storm brewing," Mum said, "I hope your dad gets home before it."

Sure, enough he did. It wasn't long before Alice wished he hadn't as it all started to go wrong then.

Alice's dad was a very proud man and loved providing for his family, they never went without anything. This meant he worked hard and was often away from the family for a few nights each week. Wednesday was usually one of them, but not tonight for some reason.

Alice wasn't sure she why as he had said he would be home Thursday when she last saw him.

As soon as he came through the door Alice could feel something was wrong and that funny feeling in her tummy grew. He was smiling as he scooped both the children up and hugged them, kissing Alice's mum on the cheek. "Hello everyone! wow!! sausage and mash for tea I'm glad I am back for that." It was a strange feeling; everyone was smiling but something wasn't right, what could it be?

Later that night as the sky turned grey and the temperature started to drop, the storm became upon them.

Billy was fast asleep in his bed and Alice was in her bed, but she was not fast asleep at all. Alice was scared, really scared.

Her mum and dad were downstairs, and she could hear an argument going on, they were shouting at each other and it just kept going on and on. Then a huge clap of thunder made her jump in her bed. In between the claps of thunder Alice could hear the argument continuing and her mum was now crying.

She couldn't make out what was being said but it didn't sound good. Her parents never argued like this, it seemed to go on for so long and was so loud.

Then a flash of lighting lit up her window and few moments later the loud bang of thunder shook the house. Hiding under her duvet Alice was crying and hoping one of her parents would appear at her bedroom door to check she was ok. They knew she hated storms.

No one appeared. Alice was heartbroken crying into Ari again, scared of the storm and scared of what was going on downstairs.

What should I do she thought? I need to check on Billy. She dried her face on her unicorn pyjamas and crept out of her bedroom into Billy's next door, he was fast asleep looking incredibly cute and none the wiser to the chaos happening in the house.

Alice sat on the top of the stairs and could hear more of the argument that was occurring.

She heard mum say, "What are we going to do now you have lost your job?"

Oh, they are arguing over money she thought. It sounded serious.

That was enough to send Alice running back to bed and straight under her duvet.

She didn't know what to do. Her parents were fighting, there was a storm and there was no money, whatever was going to happen? The sobs were so loud she couldn't stop them and thought her parents were bound to hear them and come upstairs, but they didn't.

Poor Alice became more and more upset and just wanted someone or something to be there for her. She was so scared and felt so alone.

It was then she remembered the sparkling lights from the bottom of her bed and how they made her feel safe and better when she had that bad day.

She wondered if she could make them come again, so she asked in her head. "If there is something there to make me feel safe and better, please come now."

She waited and slowly lifting her head from beneath her fairy print duvet, opening her eyes but there was nothing there. She felt so disappointed, maybe she had imagined it.

Putting her head
into Ari again. Then
she saw something
out the corner of her eye.
"What was that?" she
said. "Was that a sparkly
light?" She instantly felt hope
and sure enough the sparkles
were back.

She smiled and said "thank you" even
though she didn't know who she was
saying thank you to, all she knew is they
felt good. She was smart enough to trust
her feelings, her mum had taught her
that.

"Who are you?" She said to the sparkly lights.

She didn't hear anything, but she did get a feeling, a sort of knowingness that washed over her. "I am your Angel" was the message she got.

Alice was not sure what an Angel really was, but she had heard her nana talk about them and knew they were a good thing; she had told her everyone has them and they can help with everything. Alice knew this to be true.

"Hello Angel" she said, "Do you have a name?"

"You can call me whatever you like", was the message she felt.

"Ok" she said "I will call you Twinkle as you are like twinkly lights to me."

"Perfect" Twinkle replied and that was the start of Alice's journey with Twinkle.

That night even with all the noise and arguments Alice felt safe. She knew Twinkle would always be there for her and make her feel better, she just had to ask.

STORY FOUR

Everything always changes

Alice soon came to realise things can change very quickly in life. Nothing really stays the same. She remembers that night well when she met Twinkle and how scared and worried she was the night when her parents were arguing. Most of all she remembers how safe, cared for and looked after Twinkle made her feel. It was like a huge hug almost like her Angel wrapped their wings around her.

Alice had spoken to Twinkle every day since; she was fascinated what Twinkle could help with.

Twinkle had told her "I can help you with everything, I can make everything feel better,"

Twinkle said "and I will always keep you safe. You have nothing to worry about when you call me in to help you.

But you must ask me to help you as if you don't I can't".

"Why?" asked Alice "Because you have free will, everyone's Angels are always here to help but if you don't ask, we have to just sit back and watch you struggle".

Alice imagined that must be quite frustrating for them and she could almost see them all looking down twiddling their thumbs and having their heads in their hands. She thought I must ask them more.

"We are always giving you signs like little white feathers, but often you don't notice them because you are so busy with life".

Alice remembers how scary that night was and how in fact she had nothing to worry about in the end, it all blew over like her nana often said things did.

Her mum and dad were ok again the next morning when she woke. Later that week her dad got a new job which was local so no more going way.

Everyone was delighted and her dad was very happy.

He took all the family out for ice cream to celebrate. Her mum and dad seem so smiley and happy again. She was quite relieved as she stood at the counter deciding what to have.

Alice picked a big unicorn ice cream and her dad even let her have a flake in it. It was delicious and Alice got it all over her face as she often did when she ate. Her mum passed her a tissue to wipes the drips off her chin.

Twinkle even came along for the ice cream, Alice could feel her, she was learning that Angels are with us all the time. They are there to help when things are bad but also make good things even better.

"Do you want some ice-cream Twinkle?" Alice asked in her head. "No thanks" Twinkle laughed. "Us Angels don't need anything we are not people like you, we are just energy. We do like a thank you every now and again though." Alice smiled she. Had got quite good at chatting to Twinkle in her head now even if she often felt like she was talking to herself she knew she wasn't really.

Alice loved having Twinkle in her life and wondered why others didn't use their Angels to help them, as Twinkle had told her everyone has them, you just have to believe you do.

One day Alice was playing house in the garden with her little brother Billy. Their mum had made them a house with sheets and a clothes maiden, holding it all together with pegs. Alice had brought out her tea set and they were pretending to have tea. Of course, Ari was there with other dolls and teddies.

Alice often chatted to Twinkle in her head when she was doing other things like playing. This was no different today when she asked, "Does everyone see sparkly lights?" "No" Twinkle replied. Alice was a bit confused; "Well how do they know their Angel is there?" Alice asked. "They feel it." said Twinkle. "So many people would love to see their Angel or even hear their Angel like you do. Sadly, they think they are making it up. Everyone's Angel is always communicating with them, it doesn't matter which way but it is about trusting that feeling you get in your tummy or heart."

Alice knew it must be hard if you can't see or hear your Angel, as it wasn't that easy when Alice started to talk to Twinkle. She often thought she was making it up in her head.

Alice used to ask Twinkle to prove it to her and show her signs. "If you are real show me a sign."

"What sort of sign do you want?" said Twinkle.

"A feather" Alice said. She knew feathers were a sign of Angels as she had heard her mum and nana talk about that.

Sure, enough Alice found a feather stuck to Ari. Ari wasn't made of feathers; she didn't know where it could have come from. That was enough proof for Alice. Angels were real and she had Twinkle in her life who made her feel safe and looked after every day.

Alice never told anyone about Twinkle for a long time she didn't think that they would understand, Alice didn't really know enough about Twinkle to explain it to others, but she was excited to learn more.

CPSIA information can be obtained
at www.ICGtesting.com
Printed in the USA
BVHW020515261122
652779BV00016B/1127